FERRIS IN EXILE

Photographs by Genaro Molina
Text by Patricia Housen

Ronin Books
Santa Monica
California

Cover and back cover designed by Rikki Sax.
Edited and afterword by Robert Carney.

Library of Congress Card Number: 00-191183
ISBN 0-9700687-0-0

Printed by Regent Publishers.
Hong Kong

Ronin Books
1718 Sunset Avenue
Santa Monica, CA 90405

This book is dedicated to
Midnight and Willy.

Exile is not a material thing,
it is a spiritual thing.
All the corners of the earth
are exactly the same.
And anywhere one can dream is good,
providing the place is obscure,
and the horizon is vast.

Victor Hugo

Forward

Ferris, a Scottish Fold, has ears limp as boiled spinach. He is a powder puff of silver and white down, has green eyes big as quarters, an adobe-colored nose, and four oversized charcoal paws. Indoors would be the best place for such a lovely cat, his breeder advised. Ferris was to be a prisoner of his beauty, exiled by his lineage from the freedom common cats enjoy, destined to live out his life behind thick walls and tall fences.

He came to us with a day's supply of kitty litter — and a bad case of ringworm. A fungal infection of the skin, ringworm can be difficult to treat. "You have to shave him?" we asked, incredulously. "Well, not completely," the veterinarian said, trying to console us. "We can probably leave his whiskers."

Ferris shivered for six months that fall and winter, awaiting his fur coat. Home at the time was a bunker-like house in a quiet neighborhood. It had a back patio with sliding windows, and he would sit for hours longingly watching the birds perched on rose bushes just the other side of the screen. He hissed and puffed himself up best he could when cats wandering through the yard stopped to roll in the dirt and sun themselves.

When we finally gave in and let him out in the yard, Ferris knew just what to do. He staked his claim, stalked grasshoppers, and sniffed the day's secrets on the breeze as though he'd done it every day of his life. One day Ferris may get lucky, catch a bird and proudly leave it on the bed. We plan to praise him and tell him we know his secret: that the heart of a hunter beats in him, and that deep down Ferris, the son of Windsong and Silver Eagle, is really just an old barn cat.

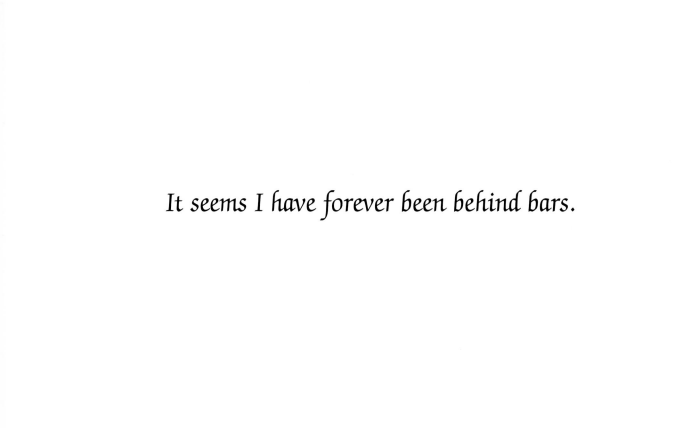

It seems I have forever been behind bars.

Shaven

and collared,

I am alone in the darkness
of a prison they call home.

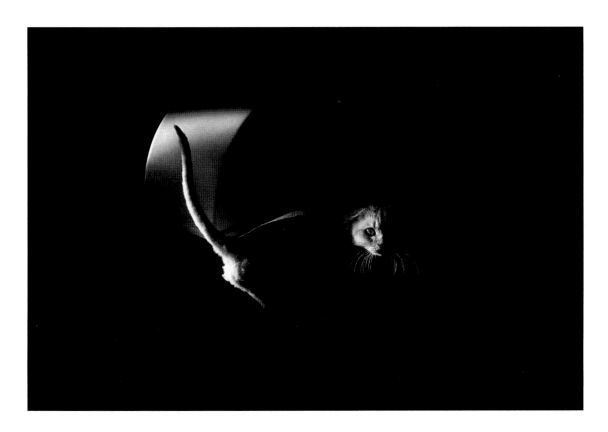

Separated from the world

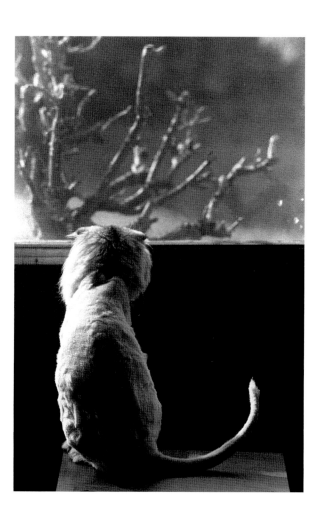

by the fine mesh they call love,

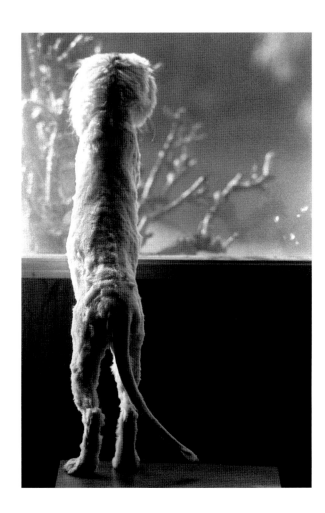

there is nothing to do but sleep

and eat.

I search for rays of hope

because who knows

what tomorrow will bring.

I reach out to touch them,

hide

and amuse them,

grow more,

ever more

beautiful

to please them.

They are forever watching me,

and I watch too.

I wait for them

in the shadows

patiently,

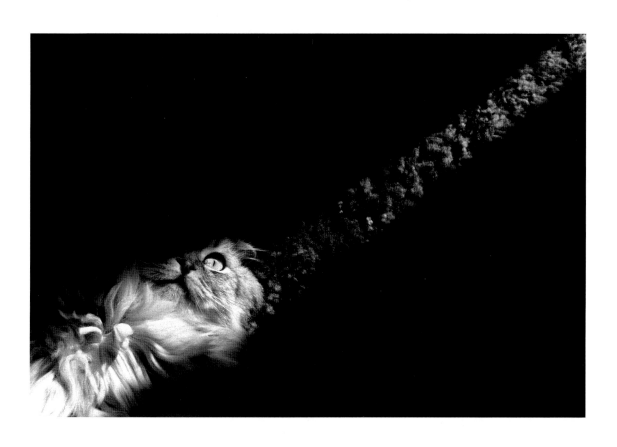

oh, so patiently,

and hopeful,

oh, so hopeful

that they will hear my heart

wishing,

and finally let me out

to savor the sunshine.

To lie in the tall grass

where I can dream

of spring

and freedom.

Afterword

All cats think they are aristocats. Unlike dogs, they don't look up to their masters, they look down upon their subjects. Of course, some felines are mere pretenders to advanced social status, but a few do have the purest of blue blood. A Scottish Fold, for example, can legitimately preen before a queen.

These cats are bred for beauty, intelligence and adaptability. So exile can be survived. It's no catastrophe. They don't become catatonic or cataleptic, even when deprived of their exquisite fur. Instead they loll in the catbird seat feasting on the catnip of guilt felt by those responsible for the shaving.

And so we cater to a cat.

That's the way the world works.

Cats rule.

Acknowledgments

We would like to thank Jonathan Nourak, Rikki Sax and Bob and Jerry Carney. Your generous contributions to this book make it sparkle.

We would also like to thank Gerry McIntyre, Michael and Robin Jones, Morgan Ong, Charr Crail, and Mark Savage for their excellent suggestions and unflagging encouragement.

Last but not least we would like to thank our parents, Ann Molina and Joseph and Ingeborg Housen. Somehow they managed to cheerfully see us through yet another book project.

About the authors:

Genaro Molina
is an award-winning photojournalist with the "Los Angeles Times".

Patricia Housen
is a writer pursuing a Ph.D. in gerontology
at the University of Southern California.

They live with **Ferris** in Santa Monica.